Piano Exam Pieces

ABRSM Grade 3

Selected from the 2015 & 2016 syllabus

Name

D0352572

Date of exam

Contents

Editor for ABRSM: Richard Jones

		page
LIST A		
1	**Muzio Clementi** Allegro: first movement from Sonatina in C, Op. 36 No. 1	2
2	**Jeremiah Clarke** The Bonny Gray Ey'd Morn	4
3	**Domenico Scarlatti** Minuet, Kp. 40	5
LIST B		
1	**Walter Carroll** A Stormy Coast. No. 7 from *In Southern Seas*	6
2	**Vladimir Ivanovich Rebikov** Pastushok na svireli igraet. No. 8 from *Siluety, detskie kartinki*, Op. 31	8
3	**Trad. Spanish** Ya se murió el burro, arr. Carol Barratt	9
LIST C		
1	**Franklyn Gellnick** Moody Prawn Blues	10
2	**Nikki Iles** Cotton Reel	12
3	**Philip Martin** Jack is Sad: from *Jack be nimble, Jack be quick…*	14

Other pieces for Grade 3

LIST A

4   **C. P. E. Bach** Allegro in C, Wq. 116/53. P. 10 from *Easy Piano Pieces – Bach* (Editio Musica Budapest)

5   **Haydn** Allegretto in E flat: No. 6 from *Différentes petites pièces (faciles et agréables)* (Edition HH) or Haydn, *Klavierstücke, Klaviervariationen* (Henle)

6   **Reinecke** Vivace: 4th movt from Sonatina in A minor, Op. 136 No. 4. Reinecke, *Six Miniature Sonatinas*, Op. 136 (Breitkopf & Härtel)

LIST B

4   **Gedike** Schulstunde (School Lesson): No. 36 from *60 Easy Piano Pieces for Beginners*, Op. 36, Vol. 2 (Peters)

5   **Kullak** Witches' Dance, Op. 4 No. 2. *The Romantic Spirit*, Book 1 (Alfred)

6   **H. Reinhold** Ariette: No. 14 from *Miniatur-Bilder*, Op. 39 (Doblinger)

LIST C

4   **Mike Schoenmehl** Melancholy: from *Little Stories in Jazz* (Schott)

5   **Seiber** Foxtrot II: from *Leichte Tänze (Easy Dances)*, Book 1 (Schott)

6   **Jesús Torres** Aurora. *Spectrum 4* (ABRSM)

First published in 2014 by ABRSM (Publishing) Ltd, a wholly owned subsidiary of ABRSM, 24 Portland Place, London W1B 1LU, United Kingdom © 2014 by The Associated Board of the Royal Schools of Music

Unauthorized photocopying is illegal All rights reserved. No part of this publication may be reproduced, recorded or transmitted in any form or by any means without the prior permission of the copyright owner.

Music origination by Julia Bovee Cover by Kate Benjamin & Andy Potts Printed in England by Headley Brothers Ltd, The Invicta Press, Ashford, Kent. Reprinted in 2015

FSC
www.fsc.org
MIX
Paper from responsible sources
FSC™ C109619

A:1

Allegro

First movement from Sonatina in C, Op. 36 No. 1

Muzio Clementi
(1752–1832)

Muzio Clementi, an English composer of Italian birth, settled in London in 1774, establishing a successful career as a pianist and teacher. His most important compositions are his keyboard works, which include about 70 solo sonatas as well as sonatinas and variations. During a continental tour as a solo pianist in the early 1780s, he stayed in Vienna for six months, taking part in a famous piano contest with Mozart. Afterwards Mozart commented on his 'remarkable technique at the keyboard'. In 1798 Clementi established a firm that not only published music but also manufactured pianos.

The six sonatinas of Clementi's Op. 36, each made up of three short movements, have long remained the most enduringly popular of his smaller and easier piano pieces. The opening movement of the first sonatina, selected here, is cast in a miniature sonata form: exposition (up to the double-bar), comprising first subject in the tonic key (b. 1) and second subject in the dominant (b. 8); development in the tonic minor (after the double-bar); and varied recapitulation (b. 24), with the second subject transposed to the tonic. All slurs are editorial suggestions only, as are the staccatos, except those of b. 30, which are present in the source. The dynamics are original, except for the editorial *crescendo* in b. 6 and the hairpins in bb. 4 and 23.

Source: *Six Progressive Sonatinas for the Piano Forte*, Op. 36 (London: Longman & Broderip, 1797)

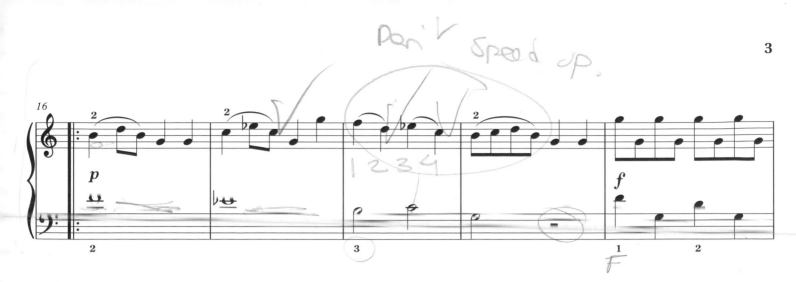

The Bonny Gray Ey'd Morn

A:2

Jeremiah Clarke
(c.1674–1707)

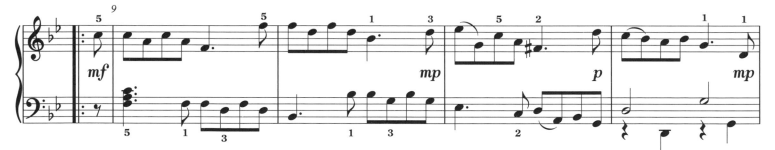

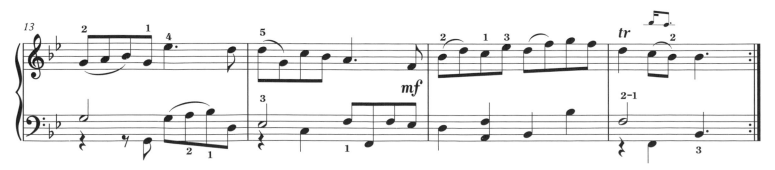

The English composer and organist Jeremiah Clarke was a chorister, and later a Gentleman, of the Chapel Royal (a member of the royal chapel that belonged to the court). In 1699 he was appointed organist of St Paul's Cathedral, London, and in 1703 Master of the Choristers there. Clarke wrote much music for the theatre, and *The Bonny Gray Ey'd Morn* originated as such: it is a keyboard arrangement of a song he had written for a revival of Thomas D'Urfey's *The Fond Husband* in 1696.

Jeremiah Clarke's own slurs in bb. 3, 8 and 16 could be played stylistically as Scotch snaps, i.e. ♫ = ♫. . In the exam this piece will work equally well with Scotch snaps in these bars (as shown above the stave), or as even quavers. All other slurs are by the editor and denote legato. The staccatos in bb. 2 and 4, as well as all the dynamics, are editorial suggestions only. All ornaments have been omitted, except for the cadential trills in bb. 8 and 16. A few small editorial adjustments have been made without comment.

Source: *The Harpsichord Master* (London: John Walsh, 1697)

© 1991 by The Associated Board of the Royal Schools of Music
Adapted from *Baroque Keyboard Pieces*, Book II, edited by Richard Jones (ABRSM)

Minuet

Kp. 40

Domenico Scarlatti
(1685–1757)

Domenico Scarlatti, Neapolitan by birth, emigrated to Portugal in 1719 and then to Spain in 1728. He spent the rest of his life in Madrid as *maestro de capilla* and music master to the young Princess Maria Barbara, who later became Queen of Spain. Most of his solo keyboard sonatas, well over 500 in number, were composed after his emigration to the Iberian peninsula.

   This minuet is one of several small pieces that the English organist and composer Thomas Roseingrave included in his edition of some of the Italian master's keyboard music, published in 1739. Roseingrave had met Scarlatti in Venice in 1709, and later popularized his music in England and Ireland. His Scarlatti edition contains some of the composer's earliest keyboard pieces, including the one selected here – relatively short and easy pieces by comparison with his later, virtuoso compositions. In this edition, all slurs and dynamics are editorial suggestions only, since there are none in the original edition.

Source: *XLII Suites de pièces pour le clavecin* (London: B. Cooke, 1739)

A Stormy Coast

No. 7 from *In Southern Seas*

Walter Carroll
(1869–1955)

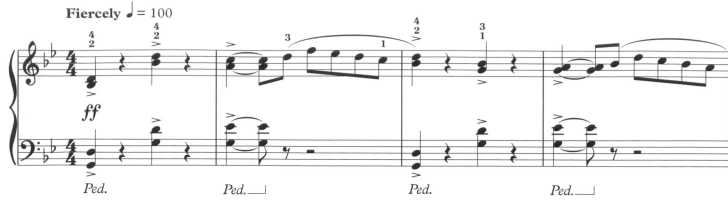

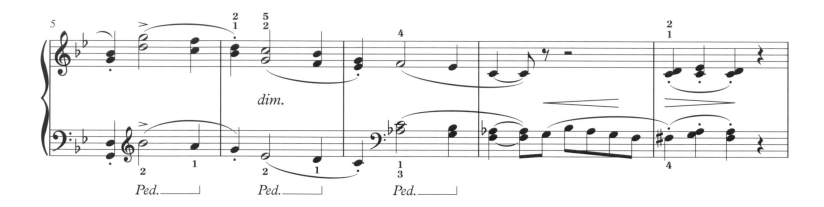

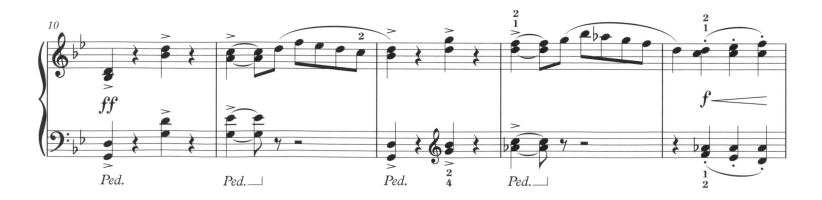

Walter Carroll was a Manchester-born music educator and composer. He played a vital role in the musical life of his native city, teaching at the Royal Manchester College of Music and at Manchester University, and acting as music adviser to the local education authority. His many fine elementary piano works include *In Southern Seas* – nine pieces with programmatic titles. They are 'sound-pictures in miniature', to borrow Carroll's description of his earlier *Sea Idylls*, also for piano.

'A Stormy Coast' is prefaced by a motto from Augusta Webster: 'Wild waves, be hushed, and moan into your rest; / Soon will all earth be sleeping, why not ye?' The composer's metronome mark is ♩ = 100, but a faster speed, for example ♩ = *c*.138, might be better suited to the 'wild waves' of the storm. Either tempo would be acceptable in the exam.

From *In Southern Seas* by Walter Carroll published by Forsyth Brothers Ltd. Used by permission of the publishers. All enquiries about this piece, apart from those directly relating to the exams, should be addressed to Forsyth Brothers Ltd, 126 Deansgate, Manchester M3 2GR.

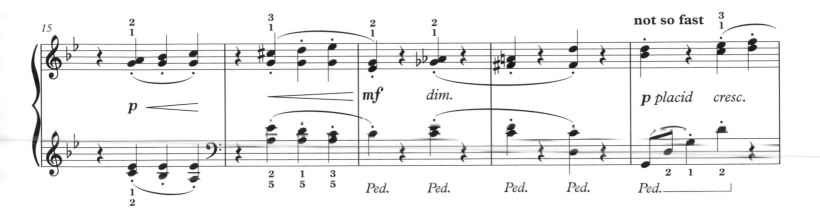

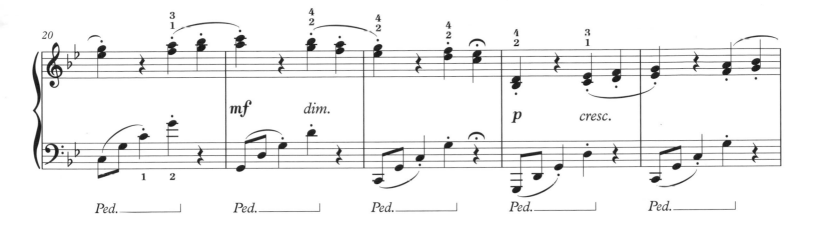

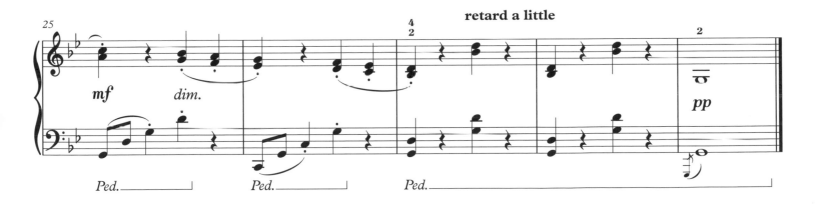

B:2

Pastushok na svireli igraet

No. 8 from *Siluety, detskie kartinki*, Op. 31

V. I. Rebikov
(1866–1920)

Pastushok na svireli igraet The Shepherd Plays on his Pipe; **Siluety, detskie kartinki** Silhouettes, Children's Pictures

The Russian composer and pianist Vladimir Ivanovich Rebikov was born during the late Romantic period, though his harmony is notably advanced for its time. He studied at the university and conservatory in Moscow and then for a further three years in Berlin and Vienna. Later he taught in various music schools in Moscow, Kiev and Odessa, and made successful concert tours as a solo pianist in both Russia and Europe.

Rebikov wrote many lyrical piano miniatures, at first influenced by Tchaikovsky and later by Debussy. These are well illustrated by the nine programmatic pieces of *Siluety*, Op. 31. In No. 8, selected here, the shepherd's tune is plaintive in the outer sections (bb. 1 and 16) but more cheerful in the middle section (b. 9). The melodic style is modal and recognizably Russian, while the rich parallel-7th chords of the central Allegretto sound strikingly impressionistic.

Source: *Silhouettes – Livre d'images en musique*, Op. 31 (Leipzig & Milan: Anton J. Benjamin, 1925)

Ya se murió el burro

B:3

Arranged by Carol Barratt

Trad. Spanish

Ya se murió el burro The Donkey has Died

This is a new piano arrangement by Carol Barratt of a traditional Spanish children's song, *Ya se murió el burro*. The words of the first verse read, in English translation: 'The donkey has died / That carried the vinegar. / God took it at last / From this miserable life.' The sad tone of the piece is perhaps due not only to the donkey's death but to the 'miserable life' he has led as a beast of burden, carrying vinegar and other goods for his master.

The key to a successful interpretation is to bring out the mournful, elegiac melody, whether it is in the right hand (bb. 3 and 19) or the left hand (b. 11), and to play it expressively. Pedal markings are suggestions by the arranger. This piece can work well with or without pedalling.

C:1

Moody Prawn Blues

Franklyn Gellnick
(born 1968)

Franklyn Gellnick was educated in Canterbury, gaining a PhD at the University of Kent in 1998. He is active as a pianist and organist, and also as an examiner for ABRSM. His interests are very wide, ranging from Gregorian chant to jazz harmony. *Moody Prawn Blues* was composed to cheer up an examiner colleague who had fallen ill during an examining trip after eating a 'moody' prawn omelette. The composer has written: 'Imagine a rather sinister, beady-eyed prawn, at a medium swing tempo, and the character of the piece should emerge.'

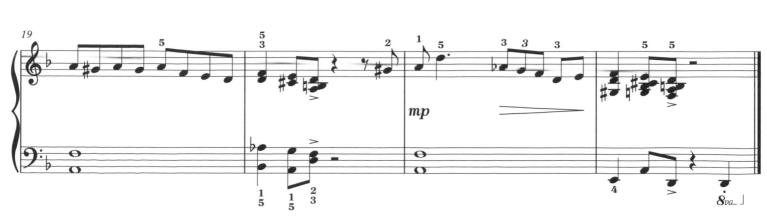

Cotton Reel

C:2

Nikki Iles
(born 1963)

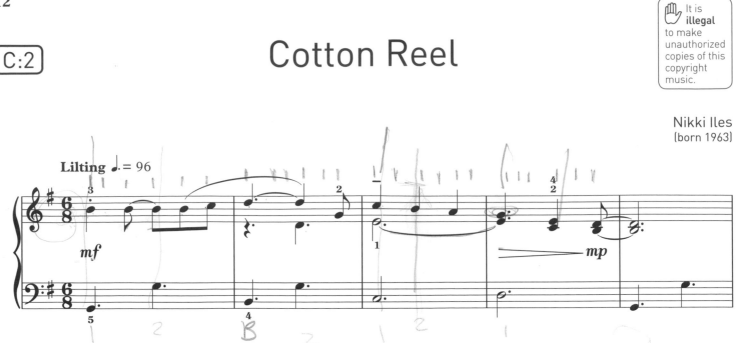

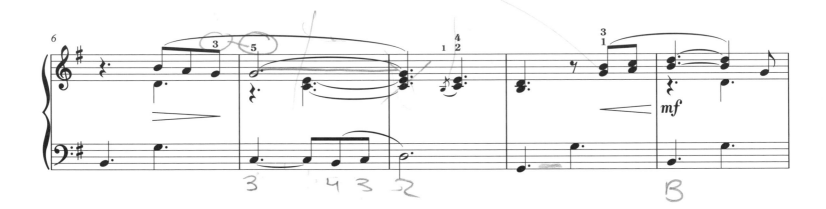

Nikki Iles is an English jazz musician, composer and pianist. At the age of 11 she won a Junior Exhibition at the Royal Academy of Music, London, studying piano and clarinet (1974–81). She went on to study alto saxophone and piano at the Leeds College of Music. As a well known jazz pianist, she has worked and recorded with many leading jazz musicians, both nationally and internationally, and has received many commissions, including those from The London Sinfonietta and the National Youth Jazz Orchestra. Very active in the field of jazz education, she holds the post of senior lecturer in jazz studies at Middlesex University and is a professor of jazz piano at the Royal Academy of Music.

About *Cotton Reel*, the composer has written: 'The secret to playing this ⁶⁄₈ dance is to feel the time signature both in dotted crotchets and in crotchets simultaneously; this fundamental cross-rhythm is common in dances of many cultures, and moving from one rhythmic grouping to another with confidence is the first step on the road to rhythmic security. The name *Cotton Reel* is a whimsical one intended to convey the flavour of this folk-like dance.'

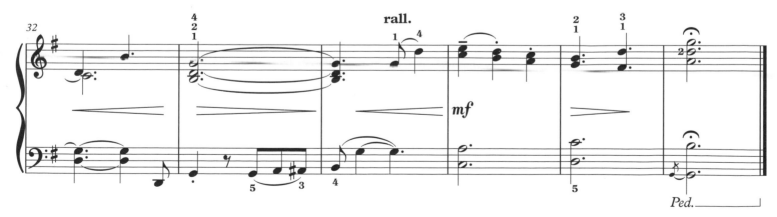

C:3

Jack is Sad

from Jack be nimble, Jack be quick…

Philip Martin
(born 1947)

The Irish pianist and composer Philip Martin was born in Dublin and studied with Franz Reizenstein, Lennox Berkeley and Richard Rodney Bennett. He now teaches piano and composition at Birmingham Conservatoire. Martin has written many instrumental works, including a symphony, four piano concertos and a harp concerto – and over 300 songs.

  'Jack is Sad' is selected from an ever-expanding collection of pieces about Jack that takes its name from the well-known nursery rhyme. This piece was written for the composer's daughter and presents the hero, Jack, in a melancholy mood. The modal style recalls Irish folk music. Although the composer's metronome mark is ♩ = 112, students may prefer a more relaxed tempo of ♩ = c.100. Either tempo would be acceptable in the exam.